Coles has served the Washington Metropolitan Community for 36 years. We provide a complete design service, including furniture, draperies, lamps, pictures, area rugs and design accessories. Our goal is to help you achieve the beautiful home of your dreams, and our design staff will make house calls on a complimentary basis to help ensure your satisfaction.

"Moments," by Drexel Heritage, represents the most up-to-date fashion statement in the home furnishings industry. Please contact our designers to help you achieve the same level of design in your home.

Moments

with

Moments

with

DREXEL HERITAGE®

LIVING ROOMS, DINING ROOMS, BEDROOMS. SPECIAL MOMENTS.

A FRESH TAKE ON FAMILY ROOMS AND HOME ENTERTAINMENT.

ACCESSORIES: CONVENIENT ONE-STOP SHOPPING FOR

ALL YOUR HOME NEEDS. PILLOWS, LIGHTING, FLOOR

COVERINGS AND BEAUTIFUL ARTWORK FOR THE WALLS.

THERE'S LIFE. And then there's living. You may have forgotten the difference. That's OK. You've been pretty busy. Showing up on time. Keeping the boss happy. Or maybe you're the boss, keeping everybody else happy. (Good luck.) But then you close the door on that life.

You're home. Ready for the Moments that you truly live for: Your daughter, shedding perfect tears because the love of her 16-year-old life hasn't called. (He will.) Your third Christmas in the new house, more beautiful than the second. Anniversaries. Birthdays. All-'A' report cards. Drexel Heritage® makes furnishings worthy of these Moments. Unmatched craftsmanship. Classic designs. Built to last a lifetime. Drexel Heritage furnishings. Welcome home.

The plot: Your life. The set:

Home movies

Your place. The cast: You and

yours, children of all ages.

Aren't you glad you're home?

THE LIVING ROOM

Remember...

"Reading 'Make Way for Ducklings' to Janie?"

A well-planned living room. Sumptuous

seating, plenty of lamps, working tables,

perhaps a patterned rug mellowed by

time. Stylish comfort for today. Lasting

impressions for the lifetime to come.

Wish you were here. A living room made for living.

Heart. Hearth. Fire. Repose. All the comforts of home.

You're looking for style. Then you see it. A few choice chairs, a touch of leather, some good wood. Nice stuff, but just informal enough to really use. Fancy that.

Rules. You've lived by enough of them to know you don't want any when it comes to your sofa. Or where you put your sofa. Or what you cover it in. Or which gorgeous armchairs you pair it with. You know what you like. You also know how you live: flexible, low-key, but with lots of style. You live by your rules. And that makes you smile.

May we have your attention?

Who among us
doesn't have a
favorite chair? You
say you don't?
Nahh...You just
haven't met it yet.

It's our pleasure to announce

that choice seats are available.

So many chairs.
So many details.
Queen Anne or
King Louis? Don't
fret. We'll have
you sitting pretty.

So, pull up a chair. We'll talk.

Remember...

"Planning the trip to the islands? We sat and talked till the sun came up."

She's yours.
Amazing. She'll
remember this
morning. Your big
hands. And the
sunny room with all
the pretty chairs.

Traditionalists insist on authentic period furniture for its historic integrity. But many of us are most comfortable with furniture that's made today but draws inspiration from traditional designs. The reason: You get to use the stuff without walking on eggs. Really use it. Dogs-and-children-in-the-same-room use it. Classic-looking pieces are also great ringers to throw into spaces that have contemporary overtones. Like family pictures saved in frames, such pieces lend warmth to any interior. And you can never have too much of that.

In Japan, elements from nature are welcome inside the house. The point? Harmony between one's home and its natural environment. It works. So do virtuous little objects that seem to have been brought in from the outdoors. Crafted from metal and stone, weathered by time, they add intriguing detail to any room.

Details, details.
Elegant finishing
touches take furni-
ture beyond the
purely utilitarian
and into the purely
satisfying.

Your place, late
morning/afternoon.
The coffee cools in
bone china cups as
the sun seeps in or
slips away. Time to
go? Not quite yet.

Artistry and tech-
niques handed
down from the
Renaissance invest
even new things
with the grand tradi-
tions of the past.

The master carver
leaves his signature
in the folds of
wood. Details that,
a century later, stir
the imagination and
collective memory.

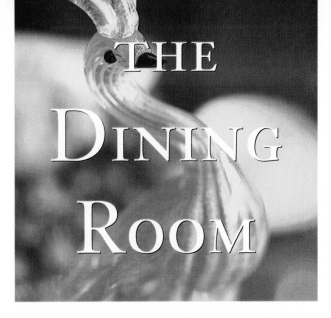

THE DINING ROOM

Pssst. Your dining room misses you.

It *has* been a while. (Hmmm. The Johnsons. Dinner. Bob spilled the Beaujolais . . . that long?) A suggestion: Don't wait for an occasion to savor your dining room. Just think of the great moments you've had there. Now, think about having them more often.

Stylish. Not dressed to

the nines. Elegant. Not

stuffy. That's your style.

Serve it with a flourish.

R e m e m b e r . . .

"Our tenth anniversary?
You sang 'How High the
Moon.' Can you believe it's
been that long?"

Come as you are,
you told them.
A casual supper.
Simple, classic
food. And a dining
room so warm, so
inviting, you knew
they'd stay late.

A host stuck in the kitchen isn't much of

a host. So, bravo for the buffet, hail to the

hutch. They look great and keep dining

essentials tableside. Such as yourself.

How to dine without reserva-

What defines a
classic? A design
that looks right
tonight, tomorrow
or twenty years
down the road.

tions: Head for the spot with

good food, great people and

Why shouldn't the
chairs you eat from
have personality?
Choose from flirta-
tious bistro style to
trim traditionals.

those lyrical chairs. Your place.

Remember...

"Our first night in the new house? Maybe it was the red wine (or the new table?), but takeout never tasted so good."

Great-looking dining
chairs are a move-
able feast. When
dinner is done,
they can bring style
and comfort to
rooms throughout
the house.

Pheasant over
glass: A glass-
topped table never
needs ironing and
provides diners
with a literal over-
view of the furniture
maker's craft.

Sun. Sweet air.
Puffy clouds in a
blue sky. A breeze
that stirs the petals
on a centerpiece.
No wonder
Americans embrace
the European tradi-
tion of alfresco
dining. Rush-bottom
seats, painted
wood surfaces and
wrought iron done
to a sophisticated
turn set the scene.

Remember...

*"Racing your sister to
the kitchen after school?
You always won.
(Only now she says
she let you win.)
No matter. You both
tasted the prize."*

Storage as charm-
ing and presentable
as what it stores
elevates function
into a thing of beau-
ty. Self-assured
curves and choice
antique finishes
turn household
workhorses into
everyday art.

When traditional South American craftsmanship is evoked, a rugged, romantic style results. The indigenous designs of the Drexel Heritage Sonora Collection are inspired by the cultures of Peru, one of the greatest civilizations of the New World. Drexel Heritage through the Masco Home Furnishings Group has formed a partnership with CARE, the world's largest relief organization, to foster CARE's programs in that country. A percentage of the sales of the "Made With CARE" Sonora Collection has been pledged by Drexel Heritage to CARE.

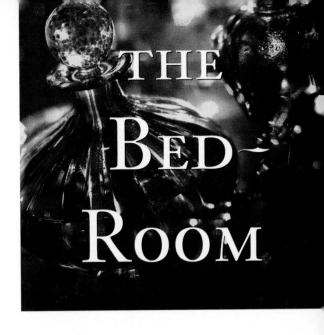

THE BED~ ROOM

Remember...

"When the dachshunds would sleep with us?"

You read there. Kiss and make up there.

You also sleep there (time permitting).

You practically live there. Aren't you

about ready for a really great bedroom?

The new bedside
manner is freestyle:
a canopy frame
without the canopy,
personal treasures
here and there,
an inviting chair.
Match them with
lavish linens, bed-
ding, pillows and
luxurious throws.

Ah, the four-poster. King of the king-

sized mattress, the sultan of sleep. The

styles may vary, but the classic look does

not: stately posts, artfully turned, sur-

rounding a bed of pure comfort.

Remember...

"Sarah's impromptu fashion show? 'Maybe she'll grow into it,' you noted. Even then, she was too cute for the room."

A bedroom built around

stylistically linked fur-

nishings is always sooth-

ing, solid and timeless.

You love traditional,
he's hooked on
modern. But don't
call the whole thing
off. Furniture that
marries traditional
cues with the clean
lines of contempo-
rary sensibilities
helps bring out
the best in each.

There's a tendency
to think of the
bedroom in literal
terms. Which literal-
ly means there are
a lot of bedrooms
out there with prac-
tically nothing in
them but beds.
Functional, if a bit
stark. But the bed-
room is, in the end,
a room—and a
mighty heavily used
room at that. So
don't neglect to
endow it with fur-
nishings, acces-
sories and decora-
tive details. Cool,
pale bureaus and
an armoire add
beauty and storage
space. But seren-
dipitous touches
are equally wel-
come, such as a
beguiling lamp or a
steamer trunk for
extra blankets.

Remember...

"Your 40th? I served you smoked salmon and a rose. You cried anyway, until the kids came in."

Picture waking up to this: An open

window, morning coffee for two and a

newspaper to linger over. A bedroom

with layers of luxurious details and quiet

style is permission to be lazy.

May we make a case for color in the bedroom? An option besides the classic white-on-white bedroom beckons. Whatever you choose, bedrooms are your personal retreat, where you can turn your style into sweet dreams.

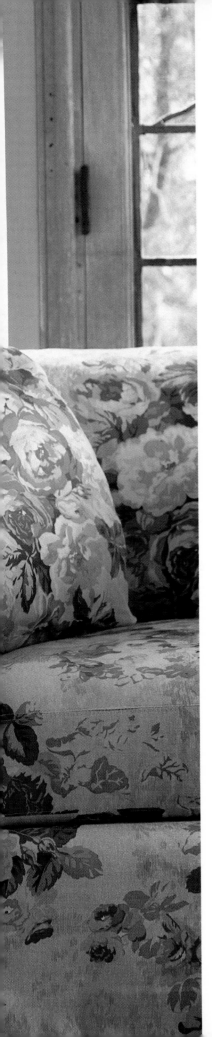

THE FAMILY ROOM

This is it. The room of rooms. The place where the threads of your household are woven into fabric that's uniquely familiar and comforting. Give the family room its due with furnishings as stylish as the days are long.

The family room of
old was the den.
Dark. Paneled.
Furnished not with
an eye toward
style but with a
hodgepodge of
castoffs trucked up
from the basement
or in from the
garage. This was
Dad's undisputed
domain for watch-
ing the Dodgers,
the birthplace of
TV-tray culture.
Today's family
room, a den no
more, is the nexus
of the home--Grand
Central with lots of
livable style. Plus
kicked-back
furnishings that
stand up to pets,
sleepovers and
teenage crushes
but snap to atten-
tion when company
comes over.

Plump upholstered
furnishings provide
the comfort level
demanded of
today's all-purpose
family room. Luxe
details like con-
trast welting, pleat-
ed skirts and
accent pillows
bring sophistica-
tion that's warm
and inviting–not
standoffish.

He already reads
like a champ. (You
don't even have to
prod anymore.) He
just climbs into that
big chair. Formal
style. Casual fabric.
Good enough for
company, friendly
enough for him and
a favorite book.

Here is furniture with a

purpose. Multi-purpose,

in fact. Fit for family liv-

ing or working at home.

Working at home? The marriage of leather, lace and classic cherry creates a home office that is corporate to the core, with all the comforts of home.

The executive suite was never quite this sweet:

Lustrous finishes. The warmest of woods. Soft-to-

the-touch leather. A desk that suits you and your

style. And enough brass to impress the Brass.

What you want. We've got it.

A

So stop putting it off. Rugs,

few

lamps, urns, gilt frames and

fine

lots more. Drexel Heritage

things

accessories. Isn't it about time?

What to Say to A Naked Floor

What would homes be without rugs? Colder. Louder. Duller. Infinitely duller. There you'd be, ready to kick up your heels, but no you-know-what to cut. Strictly aesthetically (and life without rugs is pretty strict), you'd probably miss most the color that a rug brings. Fortunately, the visual and tactile pleasures of rugs are massively enjoyed in rooms of every persuasion. In fact, large rugs establish one-third of a room's color scheme. So make sure your hankering for purple is no passing fancy.

Floor Show
Scientific facts
about rugs:
1. Amazing things
happen in rooms
furnished with
them; 2. Rugs will
cause you to win
the lottery. (Don't
quote us on #2.)

Pillow Talk

A versatile animal, the accent pillow. It can assume a sofa's stripes, an armchair's florals, or stand alone in bold, beautiful contrast. Accent pillows are the icing, but they can also be the cake, bringing style, sophistication and comfort to even the most reserved seats in the house. Pillows are the ultimate user-friendly accessory and extremely cost effective: two, or just a few, can change the whole climate of a room for the better. A tip: Vary pillow sizes, shapes and even fabrics for a rich, multilayered effect.

Support Players
Steal the Show

A room without
accessories is like
a day . . . Well, you
get the idea. They
add attitude and fill
a room's niches
with little things
that mean a lot.

Accessorize with
Color for Unity

Using color is an
easy way to orga-
nize accessories.
Blue and white
themes, for exam-
ple, are crisp, cool,
always classic.

Getting the Hang of It

Though we wouldn't presume to tell you what to hang on your walls, we can offer a few suggestions about how to hang it. (In the meantime, gaze upon the still life pictured here for inspiration.) A common mistake is hanging pictures so that they meet the eye when one is standing. Instead, hang pictures so they intercept the eyeline while sitting. When grouping pictures on a wall, trace the arrangement on paper first. Tape up this template and—voila!—you can hammer with impunity.

Seeing is Believing

Like books, music and—why not?—you yourself, art heats up a room with personality and moxie.

*They Light Up
Your Life*

Choose lamps as
you would a dinner
guest: for their abil-
ity to shed light,
their propensity for
warmth and the
color they provide.

So you don't know much about

furniture. So who does? Relax,

Nuts 'n' bolts

we do. Here's practically every-

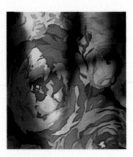

thing you need to shop smart.

You don't really need to know how an eight-way hand-tied spring works. But you should know that boring details like springs can guide you to furnishings made to the highest standards. Like those made by Drexel Heritage. In fact, the more you know about furniture, from how it's made to where it comes from, the  better our stuff looks. So here's an armchair guide, with lots of nitty-gritty. Plus, the lowdown on that spring.

Upholstered Furnishings

Take this simple test: Sit yourself down. Are you comfortable? Do you feel like staying put? Maybe even taking a little rest? (Hey . . . *hey*. We're not done yet.) "Yes" to any of the above probably means you've been cogitating in the arms of an upholstered sofa or chair. Now, Drexel Heritage knows all about these, having built them with extra-

ordinary skill for just shy of a century. So we've learned a few things along the way. Like using only extra-thick, kiln-dried hardwoods for the frames to assure long-lasting stability and structural strength. (Such a frame makes our sofas pretty darned heavy, but then, we're building them for your comfort, not the movers'.) Each spring is anchored to

the base of the frame, insulated to eliminate squeaks, then hand-tied eight, count them, eight ways. It's a time-consuming way to install springs, but it allows them to respond in unison to your every move. And that's just the inside story. Drawing from the world's finest fabric mills, Drexel Heritage maintains an inventory of more than 1,300 premium fabrics. Our upholsterers have their hands full, too, because it takes no less than 20 patterns to produce the 40 to 50 hand-cut fabric pieces needed to cover our sofas. Of course, a Drexel Heritage upholstered furnishing is offered with miles of custom tailoring options: skirt treatments, tassels, fringes, contrast pillows, the works. So you get a piece as comfortable as it is personal. And that sits well with us.

The Masters

Chippendale

Thomas Chippendale gave 18th-century English furniture shapely curves, decorated "knees" on cabriole legs, ribband-back chairs and secretaries with pediments, arches and other totems. His 1754 pattern book was considered the gospel of design.

are classics. An early cost-cutter, he applied marquetry veneers instead of gilding and used japanning to approximate exquisite lacquer finishes.

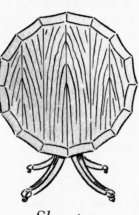

Sheraton

A Baptist minister as well as a designer, Thomas Sheraton took a "sit-up-straight" approach to his furniture design, favoring more severe lines than Hepplewhite. Decorative banding and veneers lent delicacy to his pieces, such as the canted tilt-top center table with carved pedestal base and brass-paw ferrules.

Hepplewhite

Hepplewhite shield-back chairs by Brit George Hepplewhite

How to Spot Top-Drawer Cabinetry

The hand of fine cabinet-making reveals itself in the details. Sweating the small stuff–especially the shy triumphs of craftsmanship you may never even notice–is a Drexel Heritage tradition. Like double-doweled and dovetailed joinery that lends durability and stability to dining tables, desks, secretaries and sideboards. Like solid wood weight-bearing frames, legs, posts and pedestals. Like a unique anti-sag turnbuckle that keeps dressers sitting square and level on floors that are anything but. And the details you can see? You'll be pleased to know Drexel Heritage lavishes them with the same attention. Hand-rubbed finishes that produce the sort of glow that can't be duplicated by machines alone. Expertly applied silk-screened patterns and hand-striping. Scrupulously selected and matched veneers. The richest glazing and lacquering around. It's like this: Drexel Heritage believes quality should be more than skin deep. But should you fall for one of our highboys on looks alone–we'll understand.

Leather Furnishings

Sometime, preferably soon, there really ought to be a leather-covered piece of furniture waiting for you when you come home. Why, you ask? (You have to ask?) All right. For one, genuine leather is unsurpassed as an upholstery choice. It is one of the most soothing materials to touch because it rapidly assumes your body temperature. Leather feels warm in the winter and cool in the summer—not to mention pretty terrific anytime at all. Because no two hides are alike, each leather-upholstered piece has an intrinsic personality. The variations of grain, coloration and markings—the result of years of nature's work—set real leather apart from man-made imitations. And while you may not associate

leather with practicality, the fact remains that some leather is quite resistant to everyday wear and can last five times longer than fabric. Unlike so much in life, leather even ages gracefully, acquiring a rich patina with use. And, no, leather isn't cheap. But when you stack up all the attributes, it's a long-term investment in comfort and style that you'll pat yourself on the back for years down the road. That said, Drexel Heritage has a leather-upholstered piece with your name on it. Granted, you'll have to choose from our 200 furniture styles, 17 leather patterns and 100 colors (plus generous custom options). Which could take a spell. But when you consider it takes one of our craftsmen 10 hours just to hand-tuft a single leather sofa, you'll want to take your time, too.

Let Us Entertain You

Organizing your home electronics just

got a whole lot easier (and much better

looking) thanks to the Drexel Heritage

home entertainment program.

Here's Show-Stopping Cabinetry Designed for Home Electronics

Greetings, citizens of the electronic village. We know you're in there. Up to your giga-bytes in CD players, big-screen TVs, person-al computers and fax machines. And won-dering: Why does my living room/dining room/bedroom/home office look like back-stage at a Rolling Stones concert? (Can you say, "Ugly, Exposed Cords"?) And asking: Isn't there anybody out there who makes furniture designed to hold this stuff? Glad you asked. Drexel Heritage has created a new category of furniture to do just that. Introducing the Drexel Heritage home enter-tainment program. Now, you can choose from a wide selection of beautiful and—need we add?—very functional cabinets designed expressly to hold the latest electronics equipment for home theater. And if you thought home entertainment cabinets had to be boring, bland or just plain ugly, think again. Our units feature the same craftsmanship and rich woods you'll find in all our furnishings. Styles available include Formal 18th Century, 18th Century Mahogany and 18th Century Cherry, Casual Contemporary and three styles of Country (English, French and American). Home entertainment video cabinets allow you to enjoy first-run quality without leaving the comforts of your living room. Select from freestanding armoires, cabinets with retractable pocket doors that hold up to 35-inch televisions, and units tailored to meet the requirements of direct-view and rear-projection systems with screen sizes of up to 60 inches. For concert-hall performance, minus the ticket queues and bad sight lines, home entertainment audio/video cabinets organize the multiple components typical of today's sophisticated systems. Special media storage cabinets feature compartments for videotapes, laser discs, CDs and cassette tapes. There are also bookcases, from glass-door display cabinets to open-shelf models and corner units that enhance wall systems with extra storage and great style. The Drexel Heritage home entertainment program. High tech never looked so good.

Classics

Federal
(1780–1830)

Refined neoclassical style of early American furniture makers typified by mahogany with satinwood or bird's-eye maple inlays. Patriotic designers added the American eagle to a host of classical decorative flourishes.

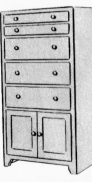

Shaker
(1860s–present)

A glory of American furniture design, Shaker arose from the 19th-century religious community: clean-lined, unadorned pieces (bureaus; the celebrated ladder-back chair) with elegant lines. "Beauty rests on utility" was the Shaker motto.

Queen Anne
(1702–1714)

Employed highly figured walnut veneers instead of ornamental inlays and carving and threw lots of curves, as in cabriole-leg and yoke-back chairs. The era also produced enduring variations on the wing chair, tea table and china cabinet (so named for the era's passion for Oriental porcelains).

Admit it. You'd love to collapse in a reclining chair like the one grandpa snoozed in. Nevertheless, you've resisted because recliners have always been . . . well, let's just say they haven't been terribly sophisticated-looking. Not anymore. Drexel Heritage manufactures no fewer than nine lines of recliners in styles ranging from traditional to contemporary. Best of all, they don't look like what you've come to expect a recliner to look like. In other words, they look like real furniture. So Drexel Heritage reclining chairs look fantastic. Are they comfortable? Let us count the features: headrests that automatically pop up when you recline; hidden controls; infinitely adjustable chairbacks that conform to your body, not vice-versa; swivel bases; "wall-hugger" designs that can be placed only inches from the wall yet fully recline. We could go on (and on). Instead, we invite you to visit your Drexel Heritage dealer for a test seating. Sit back.

The Drexel Heritage Story

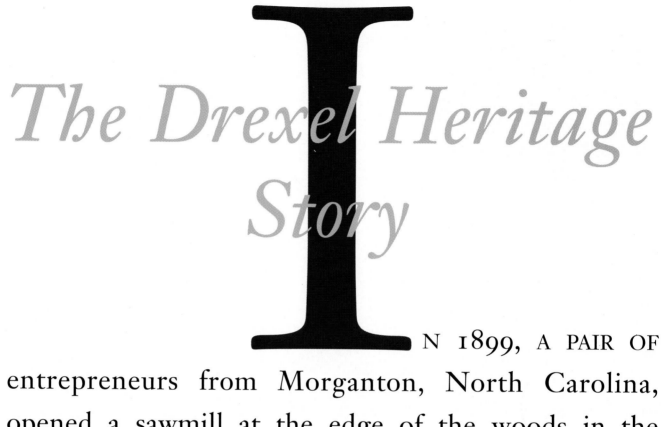

IN 1899, A PAIR OF entrepreneurs from Morganton, North Carolina, opened a sawmill at the edge of the woods in the Piedmont area. The place that Samuel Huffman and D.B. Mull had chosen to launch their business was so remote that it lacked a name. So Sam dubbed it DREXEL, after a prominent Philadelphia family he'd heard of. At first, they cut rough boards that local farmers favored for knocking together corn cribs. But Sam and D.B. had fancier plans. Noting that their little corner of the Appalachians was thick with stands of excellent hardwood, the partners raised $33,000 and, in 1903, founded the Drexel Furniture Company. Their first product–a bed, bureau and washstand suite made from native oak–sold for $14.50, wholesale. An inauspicious start, perhaps, but one that would yield a lot of great furniture over the years. Today, Drexel Heritage is a leading force in the home-furnishings field, with factories in North and South Carolina, and Drexel Heritage Home Inspirations stores and galleries throughout the country. Just as in our founding years, quality, timeless style and value remain Drexel Heritage hallmarks. Just like that three-piece suite that went for $14.50 in 1903. Sam and D.B. surely would approve.

Shopping

Anything here strike your fancy? Bet it has. Here's piece-by-

Guide

piece information on how to bring Drexel Heritage home.

THE
LIVING ROOM
Page 10

A *Heritage Collection* Sofa H1143-S

B *Heritage Collection* Slipper Chair H1477-CH

C *Heritage Collection* Exposed Wood Chair H1376-CH

D *Inheritance* Artisan's Chest 265-600

E *Inheritance* Musician Stand 265-300MAH

F *Signatures* Cocktail Table 235-108

G *Status* Lamp Table 896-300

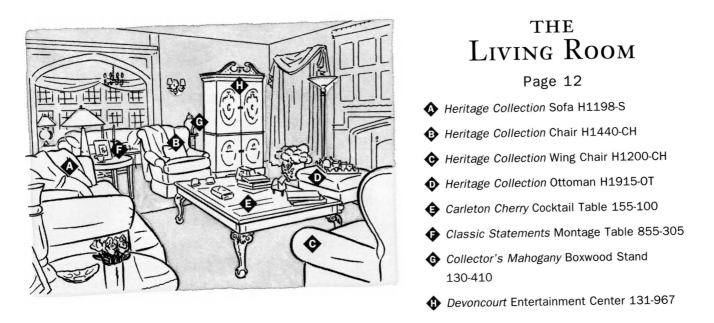

THE
LIVING ROOM
Page 12

A *Heritage Collection* Sofa H1198-S

B *Heritage Collection* Chair H1440-CH

C *Heritage Collection* Wing Chair H1200-CH

D *Heritage Collection* Ottoman H1915-OT

E *Carleton Cherry* Cocktail Table 155-100

F *Classic Statements* Montage Table 855-305

G *Collector's Mahogany* Boxwood Stand 130-410

H *Devoncourt* Entertainment Center 131-967

ALL ACCESSORIES featured in "Moments" are from the DREXEL HERITAGE accessories program. All categories of accessories found in "A Few Fine Things" are available for purchase. Our offering is fresh, exciting and inspiring–see your DREXEL HERITAGE dealer.

THE
LIVING ROOM
Page 14

A *Drexel Heritage* Leather Sofa L1074-S

B *American Themes* Armoire 606-440GRN

C *Collector's Mahogany* Jackson Cocktail Table 130-104

D *Collector's Mahogany* Edward II Night Table 110-622

THE
LIVING ROOM
Page 15

THE
LIVING ROOM
Page 23

THE LIVING ROOM
Page 24

A *Heritage Collection* Chair H1376-CH

B *Collector's Mahogany* Game Table 130-497

THE LIVING ROOM
Page 25

A *Collector's Mahogany* Oyster Bay Sideboard 120-160

B *Heritage Collection* Wing Chair H1239-CH

THE
DINING ROOM
Page 30

A *Heirlooms* Sideboard 072-164

THE
DINING ROOM
Page 33

A *Heirlooms* Highboy 070-419

B *Heirlooms* Dining Table 072-342

C *Heirlooms* Side Chairs 072-711

D *Inheritance* Ambassador's Arm Chairs
245-960MAH

THE
DINING ROOM
Page 37

◆**A** *American Themes* Side Chairs 636-961HAZ

◆**B** *American Themes* Buffet 636-120WHT

◆**C** *American Themes* Deck 636-222HAZ

◆**D** *European Themes* Toulouse Dining Table 633-346

THE
DINING ROOM
Page 43

◆**A** *Collector's Mahogany* Viceroy Dining Table 120-322

◆**B** *Collector's Mahogany* Regent Street Arm Chairs 120-714

◆**C** *Collector's Mahogany* The Kensington Buffet 120-130

◆**D** *Collector's Mahogany* The Kensington China Deck 120-230

◆**E** *Classic Statements* Monogram Arm Chairs 835-962

THE
DINING ROOM
Page 47

THE
DINING ROOM
Page 47

THE
DINING ROOM
Page 53

◆**A** *Sonora* Dining Table 448-350

◆**B** *Sonora* Arm Chairs 448-710

◆**C** *Sonora* Side Chairs 448-711

◆**D** *Sonora* The Mojave Sideboard 448-166

THE
BEDROOM
Page 55

◆**A** *Heritage Collection* Chair H1371-CH

◆**B** *Heritage Collection* Ottoman H1971-OT

◆**C** *Et Cetera* Rice Carved Bed 585-323BLK

◆**D** *Et Cetera* Hall Chest 585-038

◆**E** *Inheritance* Medallion Commode
225-632WHT

THE
BEDROOM
Page 57

A *Drexel Collection* Habitat Chair D7126-CH

B *Classic Statements* Serenity Bed 815-582

C *Classic Statements* Odyssey Commode 815-610

D *Classic Statements* Panache Table 855-416

E *Collector's Mahogany* Port Royal Chest 110-414

F *Sonora* Metal Chair 448-952

THE
BEDROOM
Page 59

A *Heritage Collection* Chair H1440-CH

B *Inheritance* Poster Bed 225-581MAH

C *Inheritance* First Edition Table 265-340MAH

D *Inheritance* Couture Dresser 225-130MAH

THE
BEDROOM
Page 63

Ⓐ *Carleton Cherry* Rice Carved Bed 105-588

Ⓑ *Carleton Cherry* Dresser 105-130

Ⓒ *Carleton Cherry* Tri-fold Mirror 105-254

Ⓓ *Carleton Cherry* Highboy 105-414

Ⓔ *Carleton Cherry* Block Front Chest 105-472

Ⓕ *Carleton Cherry* Low Chest 155-667

Ⓖ *Carleton Cherry* Bed Steps 105-780

THE
BEDROOM
Page 64

Ⓐ *European Themes* Dresser 613-120CHY

Ⓑ *Inheritance* Continental Sleigh Bed
225-592MAH

THE
BEDROOM
Page 65

◆**A** *Cabochon* Bal Harbour Poster Bed 808-582

◆**B** *Cabochon* Vista Armoire 808-440

◆**C** *Cabochon* Night Stand 808-610

THE
BEDROOM
Page 67

◆**A** *French Countryside* Bed 312-515WHT

◆**B** *French Countryside* Dresser 312-120WHT

◆**C** *French Countryside* Mirror 312-212

◆**D** *French Countryside* Armoire 312-440WHT

◆**E** *French Countryside* Night Stand
312-620WHT

THE
BEDROOM
Page 70

A *Devoncourt* Sleigh Bed 111-595

B *Collector's Mahogany* Chatham House
Chest 110-124

C *French Countryside* Octagonal Lamp Table
352-307WHT

THE
BEDROOM
Page 72

A *Collector's Mahogany* Liberty Street End
Table 130-322

B *Corinthian* Sleigh Bed 096-592

THE FAMILY ROOM

Page 77

A *Heritage Collection* Sofa H1194-S

B *Heritage Collection* Chair H1307-CH

C *French Countryside* Accessory Table 352-400

D *Signatures* Cocktail Table 234-147

E *Signet* End Table 178-003

THE FAMILY ROOM

Page 81

A *Drexel Collection* Chaise D795-CL

B *Drexel Collection* Chair D150-CH

C *Heritage Collection* Sofa H1112-S

D *American Themes* Wall Unit/Entertainment Center 862-722, 700, 710, 719, 716

E *Classic Statements* Epicurean Side Chair 835-711

F *Classic Statements* The Lyric Desk 855-507

G *Classic Statements* Architect's Cocktail Table 855-109

H *Inheritance* Console Table 265-454MAH

I *Signatures* Lamp Table 234-540

THE
FAMILY ROOM
Page 85

A *Drexel Collection* Chair D2405-CH

B *Heritage Collection* Chair H1373-CH

C *Heritage Collection* Ottoman H1373-OT

D *Classic Statements* Campaign Table 855-320

E *Classic Statements* Harlow Bench 815-730

F *Corinthian* Oval Commode 098-375

THE
FAMILY ROOM
Page 86

A *Leather Collection* Wing Chair L1120-CH

B *Leather Collection* Wing Chair L770-CH

C *Leather Collection* Ottoman L770-OT

D *Leather Collection* Executive Desk Chair L360-ST

E *Carleton Cherry* Desk 155-537

F *Carleton Cherry* Lamp Table 155-335

G *Carleton Cherry* Credenza 155-585

For more information on Drexel Heritage Home Inspirations or the dealer nearest you, please call 1-800-436-1986.

As an authorized Drexel Heritage dealer, we can promise you the superior style, quality and value synonymous with the Drexel Heritage brand name. Our partnership with Drexel Heritage also guarantees knowledgeable, dependable service and complete customer satisfaction. For peace of mind, shop only where the registered emblem is displayed.

Drexel Heritage Furnishings Inc.

A **MASCO** COMPANY

Drexel, North Carolina 28619

Printed in U.S.A.

First Edition

Editorial Director: Steven Wagner

Design Direction: Don Morris Design, New York

Text: Carol Sheehan, Michael Walker

Color photography: Michael Luppino,

Thomas Hooper

Black & white photography: John Dolan

Illustrations: James Laish

® A registered trademark of Drexel Heritage Furnishings Inc.

Published by The American HomeStyle Group, a division of Gruner + Jahr USA

George C. Fields, Jr., VP Group Publisher

David Phares, Director, New Ventures

Laurence E. Oberwager, Editor, New Ventures